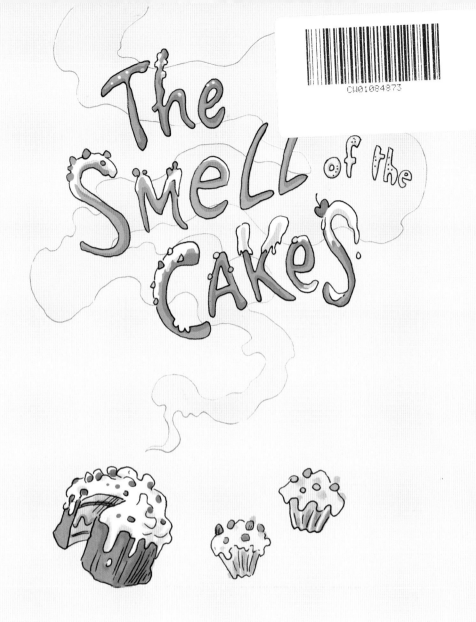

The Smell of the Cakes

A play by
Julia Donaldson

Illustrated by
Stefano Tambellini

Characters

Judge

Mr Loaf

Miss Lock

Rose Rumbletum

Clerk

Mr Freeman

Clerk: Silence in court! Silence for the judge!

Judge: It is time to hear the case of Rose Rumbletum.

Clerk: Calling Rose Rumbletum! Rose, please stand.

Judge: Rose Rumbletum, you are charged with robbery. Do you plead guilty or not guilty?

Rose: Not guilty, my lady.

Judge: Miss Lock, please begin the case.

Miss Lock: I am here to prove that Rose is guilty. I call my witness, Lenny Loaf.

Clerk: Mr Loaf, please enter the witness box.

Miss Lock: Could you tell the court what your job is, Mr Loaf?

Mr Loaf: Yes, I'm a baker. In fact, I'm the best baker in town. My cakes are very expensive, but if the judge would like one for free that's fine.

Clerk: No bribery, please!

Miss Lock: Please just tell us what happened last Monday morning.

Mr Loaf: Well, I got up at five in the morning to bake cakes. Then at nine o'clock, when I opened the shop, I spotted this girl standing outside.

Miss Lock: What was she doing?

Mr Loaf: She was just standing there, smelling the cakes.

Miss Lock: What did you say to her?

Mr Loaf: I asked her if she wanted to buy a cake, but she told me she couldn't afford it.

Miss Lock: And what did you say to that?

Mr Loaf: I told her to go away.

Miss Lock: And did she?

Mr Loaf: No, she did not. She stood there for half the morning, sniffing away, smelling my cakes without paying a penny for all those lovely smells. I call that robbery!

Miss Lock: Did you ask her to pay you?

Mr Loaf: Yes, but she just said something cheeky. And then she ran away.

Miss Lock: Thank you, Mr Loaf.

Judge: I now call upon Mr Freeman.

Clerk: Mr Freeman, please come forward.
Mr Loaf, remain in the witness box.

Mr Freeman: I am here to defend Rose Rumbletum. Mr Loaf, can you remember exactly what Rose said when you asked her to pay for smelling the cakes?

Mr Loaf: Let me think. Yes, it's come back to me. She said, "Smelling is free, isn't it?"

Mr Freeman: Thank you. I have no more questions for Mr Loaf, but I would like to ask Rose Rumbletum to enter the witness box.

Clerk: Mr Loaf, you may sit down. Rose Rumbletum, please come forward.

Mr Freeman: Rose, please tell the court in your own words what happened on Monday morning.

Rose: Well, I was out shopping for Mum. She was ill.

Mr Freeman: Were you shopping for cakes?

Rose: No, sir. We're too poor to buy cakes. I was buying bread and eggs, but I had to pass the cake shop.

Mr Freeman: And did you try to steal any cakes?

Rose: No, sir!

Mr Loaf: But she stole the smells!

Clerk: Silence in court!

Judge: Yes, please be quiet, Mr Loaf. You are not in the witness box now.

Mr Loaf: Sorry, my lady.

Mr Freeman: Rose, is it true that you stopped to smell the cakes?

Rose: Yes, it is. But I wasn't trying to steal anything. I thought that smelling was free.

Mr Freeman: Thank you, Rose. I have no more questions.

Judge: Does Miss Lock wish to question Rose?

Miss Lock: Yes. Rose, is it true that you ran away from Mr Loaf?

Rose: Yes, it is.

Miss Lock: Then you must have known that you'd done something wrong.

Rose: No, that's not true! I ran away because Mr Loaf was waving a great big loaf of bread at me. I thought he was going to hit me with it.

Judge: Do you have any more questions, Miss Lock?

Miss Lock: No, my lady.

Judge: In that case I will give my judgement.

Mr Loaf: Good! About time too!

Clerk: Silence! Show respect to the judge!

Judge: Rose, you say that you are very poor. Do you have any money at all?

Rose: Yes, my lady. I have this bag of coins. But I need the money to buy medicine for my mother.

Judge: Please hand the bag of coins to me.

Rose: But my lady ...

Judge: I will have no buts. Hand me the bag.

Mr Loaf: Great! This judge knows her stuff!

Clerk: Silence in court! Rose Rumbletum, hand your coins to the judge.

Judge: Now, I am going to shake the bag of coins. Mr Loaf, can you hear this sound?

She shakes the bag.

Mr Loaf: Yes, I can!

Judge: And I expect you liked the sound.

Mr Loaf: Yes! I liked it a lot. The sound of coins jingling is my favourite sound!

Judge: Ladies and gentlemen, Mr Loaf works very hard. On Monday he got up very early and spent four hours baking cakes. Later that morning, this girl stood outside his shop, but did she come in? Did she pay Mr Loaf for one of the cakes he had baked? No, she stood outside smelling the cakes and she did not pay him a penny.

Rose: But my lady ...

Clerk: Silence!

21

Judge: Rose Rumbletum admitted to the court that she had smelled the cakes without paying. She also told the court that she had some money – this bag of coins.

She shakes the bag again.

Mr Loaf: What a lovely sound!

Judge: Mr Loaf, you are a hard-working man and you deserve your payment.

Mr Loaf: My payment! Oh, thank you, my lady. And if you want any cakes for free, just call in at the shop.

Clerk: SILENCE!

Judge: Rose, please come here.

Rose: Yes, my lady.

Judge: Now you may have your coins back.

Mr Loaf: What do you mean? Those coins are mine! You told me they were my payment!

Judge: No, Mr Loaf. I don't think you understood. Your payment for the smell of the cakes was not the coins.

Mr Loaf: Then what was it?

Judge: It was the **sound** of the coins. Court dismissed!